D. H. LAWRENCE

Poems selected for young people.

Drawings by Ellen Raskin

D. H. LAWRENCE

Poems selected for young people

by WILLIAM COLE

MACMILLAN
London · Melbourne
1968

MACMILLAN AND CO, LTD
Little Essex Street London W.C.2
and also at Bombay Calcutta and Madras
Macmillan South Africa (Publishers) Pty Ltd Johannesburg
The Macmillan Company of Australia Pty Ltd Melbourne
The Macmillan Company of Canada Ltd Toronto

Printed in Great Britain by
Lowe & Brydone (Printers) Ltd., London

Contents

Introduction   9

Animals
    Humming-bird   17
    Snake   18
    The Elephant Is Slow to Mate   22
    Man and Bat   24
    A Living   32
    The Mosquito   34
    Self-pity   38
    Mountain Lion   39
    Butterfly   42
    Tortoise Family Connections   44
    Kangaroo   47
    The Blue Jay   50

Man, Woman, Child
    Piano   55
    Peach   57
    Discord in Childhood   58
    End of Another Home Holiday   59

The Best of School 62

The Collier's Wife 65

Celebrations and Condemnations

Conundrums 71

Thought 72

River Roses 73

How Beastly the Bourgeois Is 74

Reading in the Evening 76

Bare Fig-trees 78

The Great Newspaper Editor
to His Subordinate 83

Elemental 85

At the Window 86

A Rose Is Not a Cabbage 88

Things Made by Iron 90

All-knowing 90

Andraitx—Pomegranate Flowers 92

The Ignoble Procession 93

Last Hours 94

The Oxford Voice 96

When I Went to the Film 97

After the Opera 98

Sick 98

Bavarian Gentians 101

Love

Search for Love 105

Flapper 106

Green 108

Fidelity 109

Roses on the Breakfast Table 111

Intimates 112

Bei Hennef 114

In a Boat 115

Spring Morning 116

Index of First Lines 119

Introduction

During his lifetime, and for a long time after his death, D. H. Lawrence's poems were underrated. One reason for this was a general disbelief that a man could be one of the three or four greatest poets of this century and be at the same time a vitally important novelist and short-story writer, a penetrating literary critic, a writer of travel books, a playwright, and a painter as well. Great writers are generally blessed with one, or at most two, gifts. Such raging and ranging genius as Lawrence had blinds the onlooker.

Another reason for his not being appreciated in his time was that he wrote so very much; poems flowed from him; his recently-published *Complete Poems* is in two large volumes, and contains about a thousand poems. He was never "blocked"; he never forced a poem. A poem was to him simply one way of expressing himself; he gave his poems a value neither more nor less than his fiction and other writings; they were part of his being. He believed that he wrote two quite different kinds of poems—his "real poems" and his "compositions." In the Foreword to his *Collected Poems* he talks about composing his first two poems when he was nineteen: ". . . and most young ladies would have done better: at least I hope so. But I thought the effusions very nice . . ." Then, as he wrote more poetry, a change took place: "I used to feel myself at times haunted by something, and a little guilty about it, as if it were an abnormality. Then the haunting would get the better of me, and the ghost would suddenly appear, in the shape of a usually rather incoherent poem. Nearly always I shunned the apparition once it had appeared. From the first, I was a little afraid of my real poems—not my 'compositions,' but the poems that had the ghost in them. They seemed to me to come from somewhere, I didn't quite know where, out of a me whom I didn't know and didn't want to know, and to say things I would much rather not have said: for choice. But there they were." He refers to this ghost, this haunting, as "the demon," and talks about how, for his collected volume, he changed some poems "to get them into better form, and take out the dead bits. It took me many years," he wrote, "to learn to play with the form of a poem: even if I can do it now. But it is only in the less immediate, the more fictional poems that the form has to be played with. The demon, when he's really there, makes his own form willy-nilly, and is unchangeable."

The literary critics during Lawrence's earlier years weren't having any of that. They refused to believe that a poem appeared in some unusual form because there was a "demon" in it. It was a generally pallid poetic era, and he was simply too unconventional for them. He complained to the American poet Amy Lowell in 1917 when his *Look! We Have Come Through!* was published: "As usual the critics fall on me: *The Times* says 'the Muse can only turn away her face in pained distaste.' Poor Muse, I feel as if I have affronted a white-haired old spinster with weak eyes." What the critics did not realize was that they were dealing with one of the geniuses of all time, and that a genius creates his own forms, and *has* to speak in his own voice. And his scorn for the critics—sometimes in print—certainly did nothing to endear him to them. It is also a point that Lawrence's other literary activities—his novels were shockingly frank about sex, for those times—bedazzled and horrified the critics and set off much louder explosions than the poems.

Lawrence's best poems are those that have, in his expression, "organic form." They are loose in construction; they follow no rules. He said, "Much has been written about free verse. But all that can be said, first and last, is that free verse is, or should be, direct utterance from the instant, whole man. It is the soul and the mind and the body surging at once, nothing left out." Many of his, as he called them, "rhyming poems" are wonderful, but his real voice is heard only when he writes without the restrictions of rhyme, when nothing gets between himself and the poem. Some of his poems are simple statements, as though he were talking to the reader as a good friend; others are blasts of invective, and still others are complex, difficult—they mean what they say on the first level, but they don't mean *only* that.

Lawrence's affection, his reverence for life, comes through best in his animal poems. Whenever he starts writing about man, he gets mad; he is enraged at the difference between what man could be—should be—and what he is. But the animals never disappoint; they are never self-pitying or hypocritical. They are "as incapable of telling lies as fire is." It is unimportant that he frequently invests his animals with human qualities, and that he isn't always anatomically exact—the idea of a snake having shoulders is certainly an interesting one. He knows how to pluck just the right word to give a picture of *that* animal—the bat, with "cluttered fear," as it is "flicker-splashing around my room"; the mosquito with his "small, high, hateful bugle in my ear." He calls to that "perambulating pebble," the baby tortoise, "Whither away, brisk egg?" There is an uncanny immediacy about the poems; "The Bat," for example, seems to unfold on the page before the reader; it is almost as though Lawrence were sitting with you, telling you excitedly about something that happened to him just a few hours ago, and when he comes to the point where the exhausted bat falls to the floor, and he doesn't know what to do with it, he exclaims, "So, a dilemma!" and you find yourself thinking ahead, trying to solve that dilemma for him. He speaks of birds, beasts, flowers, and fishes with love and respect, and always with wit. Aldous Huxley, who knew him well, wrote that "he seemed to know, by personal experience, what it was like to be a tree or a daisy or a breaking wave or even the mysterious moon itself. He could get inside the skin of an animal and tell you in the most convincing detail how it felt and how, dimly, inhumanly, it thought."

Lawrence was a prophet-poet, as were the great poets he admired, Blake and Whitman. He was a red-bearded preacher, a tub-thumper, forever exhorting, railing, extolling. He never guessed, he always *knew*. This made him a hard man to be around, yet, from all accounts, an eternally fascinating one. His magnetism drew people to him; his frankness about them frequently drove them away. He couldn't stand prissiness, people with "cold guts and over-squeamish minds." He said, "My great belief is in the blood, the flesh, as being wiser than the intellect. We can go wrong in our minds. But what our blood feels and believes and says, is always true." But the American poet Adrienne Rich recently pointed out that ". . . this hero of the instinctual was one of the most intelligent men of any time." He was that rarity, a man as interesting to read *about* as to read. It seems that nobody could meet him without having a later compulsion to write about the experience.

D. H. Lawrence—David Herbert—was born in the village of Eastwood, Nottinghamshire, England, in 1885. His father was a miner, hard-working, coarse, and a drinker. His mother was an ex-schoolteacher, genteel and frail, who felt that she had married below her station. Lawrence, the fourth of five children, was always sickly, and always over-protected by his mother. His childhood nickname was "Mardy"—Nottingham dialect for "petted." He has written that his relationship with his mother was the most profound thing in his life, and her death, in 1910, brought on a severe depression; because of it, he gave up teaching, which had become his profession. It was a profession he didn't care much for; his explosive creative energy needed further outlets. He had begun writing in 1906; his first novel, *The White Peacock*, was published in 1911. In an amusing and revealing sidelight, Lawrence recalls his father's reaction upon hearing that the publisher had given him an advance of fifty pounds: "He looked at me with shrewd eyes, as if I were a swindler. 'Fifty pounds! An' tha's niver done a day's work in thy life!'" In 1912 Lawrence met Frieda Weekley, a married woman six years his senior, the daughter of the German Baron Friedrich von Richtofen. Two years later, after her divorce, they were married and began a tumultuous life together. Lawrence was always on the move—from Italy to Germany to France to England and back to Italy again—always looking for a place in which he could feel at ease, and never finding it. They went to Australia, they went to Ceylon, and twice in a four-year period they lived in America—in New Mexico and Mexico, which were, to Lawrence, the best places of all. Although he was writing and publishing continually, he was always beset with money problems. But even more debilitating to his spirit was the censorship imposed on his more outspoken novels—books that are published today with hardly a murmur, but which were regarded as sinful in the 1920s. Some half-dozen friends remained close to him all his life, and his exciting letters—the best of our century— to those friends and to others are collected in two packed volumes. The writer Katherine Mansfield, whose long friendship with him had its ups and downs, wrote that late in their friendship, when she was sick, he used to come to cheer her up daily, and that he was "just his old, merry, rich self, laughing, describing things, giving you pictures, full of enthusiasm and joy in a future where we become all 'vagabonds' . . . oh, there is something so lovable about him and his eagerness, his passionate eagerness for life—and that is what one loves so." And he and Frieda would fight—spectacularly, from some reports—but always make up quickly. In his fine biography of Lawrence, *The Intelligent Heart*, Harry T. Moore gives one amusing eye-witness report: "Lawrence had begun singing, thinking the quarrel was over, when Frieda came up behind him . . . and bashed him with a stone dinner plate." Something of his mischievousness in his lighter moments is in the poems "Intimates" and "Peach," which are certainly about his marriage.

13

In 1926 Lawrence and Frieda settled for two years in a villa near Florence, Italy. He was terribly ill from tuberculosis, but worked with undiminished fervor. It was there that he completed *Lady Chatterley's Lover,* and wrote many of his most intensely beautiful poems. He had also taken up painting seriously. In 1928 they moved one last time, to southern France, where Lawrence died in 1930. He was buried in the local cemetery, and five years later his remains were cremated, and his ashes brought to New Mexico, where they are in a tomb overlooking the Rio Grande. His name is also engraved on the family tombstone in Eastwood, with the inscription "novelist poet painter" under which in large letters is the word "unconquered." A fitting epitaph, certainly, but perhaps even more fitting epitaphs are found in the words of those friends who loved him and learned from him. To quote Aldous Huxley again: "For wherever he looked, he saw more than a human being ought to see; saw more and therefore loved and hated more. To be with him was to find oneself transported to one of the frontiers of human consciousness. For an inhabitant of the safe metropolis of thought and feeling it was a most exciting experience."

Animals

Humming-bird

I can imagine, in some otherworld
Primeval-dumb, far back
In that most awful stillness, that only gasped and hummed,
Humming-birds raced down the avenues.

Before anything had a soul,
While life was a heave of Matter, half inanimate,
This little bit chipped off in brilliance
And went whizzing through the slow, vast, succulent stems.

I believe there were no flowers then,
In the world where the humming-bird flashed ahead of creation.
I believe he pierced the slow vegetable veins with his long beak.

Probably he was big
As mosses, and little lizards, they say, were once big.
Probably he was a jabbing, terrifying monster.

We look at him through the wrong end of the long telescope of Time,
Luckily for us.

Snake

A snake came to my water-trough
On a hot, hot day, and I in pyjamas for the heat,
To drink there.

In the deep, strange-scented shade of the great dark carob-tree
I came down the steps with my pitcher

And must wait, must stand and wait, for there he was at the
    trough before me.

He reached down from a fissure in the earth-wall in the gloom
And trailed his yellow-brown slackness soft-bellied down, over
    the edge of the stone trough
And rested his throat upon the stone bottom,
And where the water had dripped from the tap, in a small clear-
    ness,
He sipped with his straight mouth,

Softly drank through his straight gums, into his slack long body,
Silently.

Someone was before me at my water-trough,
And I, like a second comer, waiting.

He lifted his head from his drinking, as cattle do,
And looked at me vaguely, as drinking cattle do,
And flickered his two-forked tongue from his lips, and mused a
    moment,

And stooped and drank a little more,
Being earth-brown, earth-golden from the burning bowels of
    the earth
On the day of Sicilian July, with Etna smoking.

The voice of my education said to me
He must be killed,
For in Sicily the black, black snakes are innocent, the gold are
    venomous.

And voices in me said, If you were a man
You would take a stick and break him now, and finish him off.

But must I confess how I liked him,
How glad I was he had come like a guest in quiet, to drink at
    my water-trough
And depart peaceful, pacified, and thankless,
Into the burning bowels of this earth?

Was it cowardice, that I dared not kill him?
Was it perversity, that I longed to talk to him?
Was it humility, to feel so honoured?
I felt so honoured.

And yet those voices:
If you were not afraid, you would kill him!

And truly I was afraid, I was most afraid,
But even so, honoured still more
That he should seek my hospitality
From out the dark door of the secret earth.

He drank enough
And lifted his head, dreamily, as one who has drunken,
And flickered his tongue like a forked night on the air, so
    black;
Seeming to lick his lips,
And looked around like a god, unseeing, into the air,
And slowly turned his head,
And slowly, very slowly, as if thrice adream,
Proceeded to draw his slow length curving round
And climb again the broken bank of my wall-face.

And as he put his head into that dreadful hole,
And as he slowly drew up, snake-easing his shoulders, and en-
    tered farther,

A sort of horror, a sort of protest against his withdrawing into
    that horrid black hole,
Deliberately going into the blackness, and slowly drawing him-
    self after,
Overcame me now his back was turned.

I looked round, I put down my pitcher,
I picked up a clumsy log
And threw it at the water-trough with a clatter.

I think it did not hit him,
But suddenly that part of him that was left behind convulsed
    in undignified haste,
Writhed like lightning, and was gone
Into the black hole, the earth-lipped fissure in the wall-front,
At which, in the intense still noon, I stared with fascination.

And immediately I regretted it.
I thought how paltry, how vulgar, what a mean act!
I despised myself and the voices of my accursed human educa-
    tion.

And I thought of the albatross,
And I wished he would come back, my snake.

For he seemed to me again like a king,
Like a king in exile, uncrowned in the underworld,
Now due to be crowned again.

And so, I missed my chance with one of the lords
Of life.
And I have something to expiate;
A pettiness.

The Elephant Is Slow to Mate

The elephant, the huge old beast,
    is slow to mate;
he finds a female, they show no haste
    they wait

for the sympathy in their vast shy hearts
    slowly, slowly to rouse
as they loiter along the river-beds
    and drink and browse

and dash in panic through the brake
    of forest with the herd,
and sleep in massive silence, and wake
    together, without a word.

So slowly the great hot elephant hearts
    grow full of desire,
and the great beasts mate in secret at last,
    hiding their fire.

Oldest they are and the wisest of beasts
    so they know at last
how to wait for the loneliest of feasts
    for the full repast.

They do not snatch, they do not tear;
    their massive blood
moves as the moon-tides, near, more near,
    till they touch in flood.

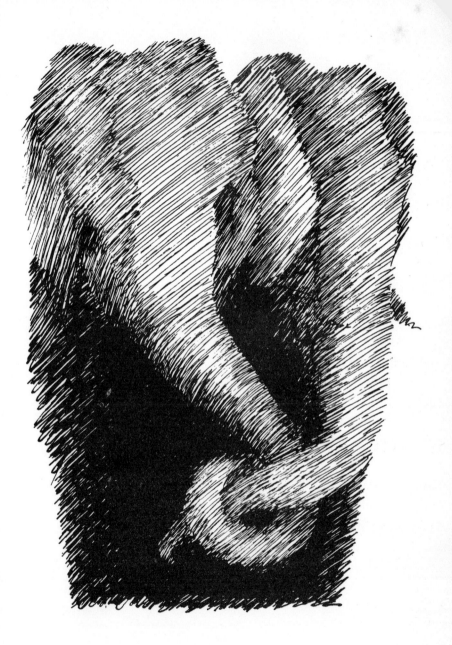

Man and Bat

When I went into my room, at mid-morning,
Say ten o'clock . . .
My room, a crash-box over that great stone rattle
The Via de' Bardi. . . .

When I went into my room at mid-morning,
Why? . . . a bird!

A bird
Flying round the room in insane circles.

In insane circles!
. . . A bat!

A disgusting bat
At mid-morning! . . .

Out! Go out!

Round and round and round
With a twitchy, nervous, intolerable flight,
And a neurasthenic lunge,
And an impure frenzy;
A bat, big as a swallow.

Out, out of my room!

The venetian shutters I push wide
To the free, calm upper air;
Loop back the curtains. . . .

Now out, out from my room!

So to drive him out, flicking with my white handkerchief: *Go!*
But he will not.

Round and round and round
In an impure haste,
Fumbling, a beast in air,
And stumbling, lunging and touching the walls, the bell-wires
About my room!
Always refusing to go out into the air
Above that crash-gulf of the Via de' Bardi,
Yet blind with frenzy, with cluttered fear.

At last he swerved into the window bay,
But blew back, as if an incoming wind blew him in again.
A strong inrushing wind.

And round and round and round!
Blundering more insane, and leaping, in throbs, to clutch at a
    corner,
At a wire, at a bell-rope:
On and on, watched relentless by me, round and round in my
    room,

Round and round and dithering with tiredness and haste and
    increasing delirium
Flicker-splashing round my room.

I would not let him rest;
Not one instant cleave, cling like a blot with his breast to the
    wall
In an obscure corner.
Not an instant!

I flicked him on,
Trying to drive him through the window.
Again he swerved into the window bay
And I ran forward, to frighten him forth.
But he rose, and from a terror worse than me he flew past me
Back into my room, and round, round, round in my room
Clutch, cleave, stagger,
Dropping about the air
Getting tired.

Something seemed to blow him back from the window
Every time he swerved at it;
Back on a strange parabola, then round, round, dizzy in my
    room.

He *could* not go out,
I also realised. . . .
It was the light of day which he could not enter,
Any more than I could enter the white-hot door of a blast fur-
nace.

He could not plunge into the daylight that streamed at the
window.
It was asking too much of his nature.

Worse even than the hideous terror of me with my handker-
chief
Saying: *Out, go out!* . . .
Was the horror of white daylight in the window!

So I switched on the electric light, thinking: *Now*
The outside will seem brown. . . .

But no.
The outside did not seem brown.
And he did not mind the yellow electric light.

Silent!
He was having a silent rest.
But never!
Not in my room.

27

Round and round and round
Near the ceiling as if in a web,
Staggering;
Plunging, falling out of the web,
Broken in heaviness,
Lunging blindly,
Heavier;
And clutching, clutching for one second's pause,
Always, as if for one drop of rest,
One little drop.

And I!
Never, I say. . . .
Get out!

Flying slower,
Seeming to stumble, to fall in air.
Blind-weary.

Yet never able to pass the whiteness of light into freedom . . .
A bird would have dashed through, come what might.

Fall, sink, lurch, and round and round
Flicker, flicker-heavy;
Even wings heavy:
And cleave in a high corner for a second, like a clot, also a
    prayer.

But no.
Out, you beast.

Till he fell in a corner, palpitating, spent.
And there, a clot, he squatted and looked at me.
With sticking-out, bead-berry eyes, black,
And improper derisive ears,
And shut wings,
And brown, furry body.

Brown, nut-brown, fine fur!
But it might as well have been hair on a spider; thing
With long, black-paper ears.

So, a dilemma!
He squatted there like something unclean.

No, he must not squat, nor hang, obscene, in my room!

Yet nothing on earth will give him courage to pass the sweet
fire of day.

What then?
Hit him and kill him and throw him away?

Nay,
I didn't create him.
Let the God that created him be responsible for his death . . .
Only, in the bright day, I will not have this clot in my room.

Let the God who is maker of bats watch with them in their unclean corners. . . .
I admit a God in every crevice,

But not bats in my room;
Nor the God of bats, while the sun shines.

So out, out, you brute! . . .
And he lunged, flight-heavy, away from me, sideways, *a sghembo!*
And round and round and round my room, a clot with wings,
Impure even in weariness.

Wings dark skinny and flapping the air,
Lost their flicker.
Spent.

He fell again with a little thud
Near the curtain on the floor.
And there lay.

Ah death, death
You are no solution!
Bats must be bats.

Only life has a way out.
And the human soul is fated to wide-eyed responsibility
In life.

So I picked him up in a flannel jacket,
Well covered, lest he should bite me.
For I would have had to kill him if he'd bitten me, the impure
    one. . . .
And he hardly stirred in my hand, muffled up.

Hastily, I shook him out of the window.

And away he went!
Fear craven in his tail.
Great haste, and straight, almost bird straight above the Via de'
    Bardi.
Above that crash-gulf of exploding whips,
Towards the Borgo San Jacopo.

And now, at evening, as he flickers over the river
Dipping with petty triumphant flight, and tittering over the
    sun's departure,
I believe he chirps, pipistrello, seeing me here on this terrace
    writing:
There he sits, the long loud one!
But I am greater than he . . .
I escaped him. . . .

A Living

A man should never earn his living,
if he earns his life he'll be lovely.

A bird
picks up its seeds or little snails
between heedless earth and heaven
in heedlessness.

But, the plucky little sport, it gives to life
song, and chirruping, gay feathers, fluff-shadowed warmth
and all the unspeakable charm of birds hopping and fluttering
    and being birds.
—And we, we get it all from them for nothing.

The Mosquito

When did you start your tricks,
Monsieur?

What do you stand on such high legs for?
Why this length of shredded shank,
You exaltation?

Is it so that you shall lift your centre of gravity upwards
And weigh no more than air as you alight upon me,
Stand upon me weightless, you phantom?

I heard a woman call you the Winged Victory
In sluggish Venice.
You turn your head towards your tail, and smile.

How can you put so much devilry
Into that translucent phantom shred
Of a frail corpus?

Queer, with your thin wings and your streaming legs,
How you sail like a heron, or a dull clot of air,
A nothingness.

Yet what an aura surrounds you;
Your evil little aura, prowling, and casting numbness on my
    mind.
That is your trick, your bit of filthy magic:
Invisibility, and the anæsthetic power
To deaden my attention in your direction.

But I know your game now, streaky sorcerer.
Queer, how you stalk and prowl the air
In circles and evasions, enveloping me,
Ghoul on wings
Winged Victory.

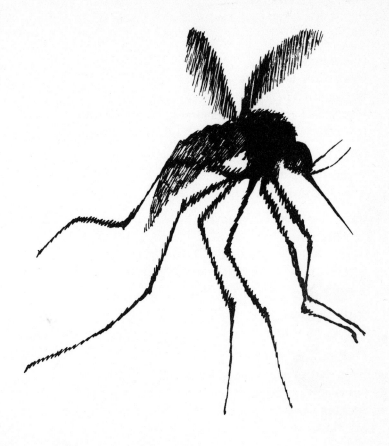

Settle, and stand on long thin shanks
Eyeing me sideways, and cunningly conscious that I am aware,
You speck.

I hate the way you lurch off sideways into the air
Having read my thoughts against you.

Come then, let us play at unawares,
And see who wins in this sly game of bluff.
Man or mosquito.

You don't know that I exist, and I don't know that you exist.
Now then!

It is your trump,
It is your hateful little trump,
You pointed fiend,
Which shakes my sudden blood to hatred of you:
It is your small, high, hateful bugle in my ear.

Why do you do it?
Surely it is bad policy.
They say you can't help it.

If that is so, then I believe a little in Providence protecting the
    innocent.
But it sounds so amazingly like a slogan,
A yell of triumph as you snatch my scalp.

Blood, red blood
Super-magical
Forbidden liquor.

I behold you stand
For a second enspasmed in oblivion,
Obscenely ecstasied
Sucking live blood,
My blood.

Such silence, such suspended transport,
Such gorging,
Such obscenity of trespass.

You stagger
As well you may.
Only your accursed hairy frailty,
Your own imponderable weightlessness

Saves you, wafts you away on the very draught my anger makes
    in its snatching.

Away with a pæan of derision,
You winged blood-drop.

Can I not overtake you?
Are you one too many for me,
Winged Victory?
Am I not mosquito enough to out-mosquito you?

Queer what a big stain my sucked blood makes
Beside the infinitesimal faint smear of you!
Queer, what a dim dark smudge you have disappeared into!

Self-pity

I never saw a wild thing
sorry for itself.
A small bird will drop frozen dead from a bough
without ever having felt sorry for itself.

Mountain Lion

Climbing through the January snow, into the Lobo Canyon
Dark grow the spruce-trees, blue is the balsam, water sounds
    still unfrozen, and the trail is still evident.

Men!
Two men!
Men! The only animal in the world to fear!

They hesitate.
We hesitate.
They have a gun.
We have no gun.

Then we all advance, to meet.

Two Mexicans, strangers, emerging out of the dark and snow
    and inwardness of the Lobo valley.
What are they doing here on this vanishing trail?

What is he carrying?
Something yellow.
A deer?

Qué tiene, amigo?
León—

He smiles, foolishly, as if he were caught doing wrong.
And we smile, foolishly, as if we didn't know.
He is quite gentle and dark-faced.

It is a mountain lion,
A long, long slim cat, yellow like a lioness.
Dead.

He trapped her this morning, he says, smiling foolishly.

Lift up her face,
Her round, bright face, bright as frost.
Her round, fine-fashioned head, with two dead ears;
And stripes in the brilliant frost of her face, sharp, fine dark
    rays,
Dark, keen, fine rays in the brilliant frost of her face.
Beautiful dead eyes.

Hermoso es!

They go out towards the open;
We go on into the gloom of Lobo.

And above the trees I found her lair,
A hole in the blood-orange brilliant rocks that stick up, a little
    cave.
And bones, and twigs, and a perilous ascent.

So, she will never leap up that way again, with the yellow flash
    of a mountain lion's long shoot!
And her bright striped frost-face will never watch any more,
    out of the shadow of the cave in the blood-orange rock,
Above the trees of the Lobo dark valley-mouth!

Instead, I look out.
And out to the dim of the desert, like a dream, never real;
To the snow of the Sangre de Cristo mountains, the ice of the
    mountains of Picoris,
And near across at the opposite steep of snow, green trees mo-
    tionless standing in snow, like a Christmas toy.

And I think in this empty world there was room for me and a
    mountain lion.
And I think in the world beyond, how easily we might spare a
    million or two of humans
And never miss them.
Yet what a gap in the world, the missing white frost-face of that
    slim yellow mountain lion!

Butterfly

Butterfly, the wind blows sea-ward, strong beyond the garden
   wall!
Butterfly, why do you settle on my shoe, and sip the dirt on my
   shoe,
Lifting your veined wings, lifting them? big white butterfly!

Already it is October, and the wind blows strong to the sea
from the hills where snow must have fallen, the wind is polished
   with snow.
Here in the garden, with red geraniums, it is warm, it is warm
but the wind blows strong to sea-ward, white butterfly, content
   on my shoe!

Will you go, will you go from my warm house?
Will you climb on your big soft wings, black-dotted,
as up an invisible rainbow, an arch
till the wind slides you sheer from the arch-crest
and in a strange level fluttering you go out to sea-ward, white
   speck!

Farewell, farewell, lost soul!
you have melted in the crystalline distance,
it is enough! I saw you vanish into air.

Tortoise Family Connections

On he goes, the little one,
Bud of the universe,
Pediment of life.

Setting off somewhere, apparently.
Whither away, brisk egg?

His mother deposited him on the soil as if he were no more
    than droppings,
And now he scuffles tinily past her as if she were an old rusty
    tin.

A mere obstacle,
He veers round the slow great mound of her—
Tortoises always foresee obstacles.

It is no use my saying to him in an emotional voice:
"This is your Mother, she laid you when you were an egg."

He does not even trouble to answer: "Woman, what have I to
    do with thee?"
He wearily looks the other way,
And she even more wearily looks another way still,
Each with the utmost apathy,
Incognisant,
Unaware,
Nothing.

As for papa,
He snaps when I offer him his offspring,
Just as he snaps when I poke a bit of stick at him,
Because he is irascible this morning, an irascible tortoise
Being touched with love, and devoid of fatherliness.

Father and mother,
And three little brothers,
And all rambling aimless, like little perambulating pebbles
    scattered in the garden,
Not knowing each other from bits of earth or old tins.

Except that papa and mama are old acquaintances, of course,
Though family feeling there is none, not even the beginnings.
Fatherless, motherless, brotherless, sisterless
Little tortoise.

Row on then, small pebble,
Over the clods of the autumn, wind-chilled sunshine,
Young gaiety.

Does he look for a companion?

No, no, don't think it.
He doesn't know he is alone;
Isolation is his birthright,
This atom.

To row forward, and reach himself tall on spiny toes,
To travel, to burrow into a little loose earth, afraid of the
      night,
To crop a little substance,
To move, and to be quite sure that he is moving:
Basta!
To be a tortoise!
Think of it, in a garden of inert clods
A brisk, brindled little tortoise, all to himself—
Adam!

In a garden of pebbles and insects
To roam, and feel the slow heart beat
Tortoise-wise, the first bell sounding
From the warm blood, in the dark-creation morning.

Moving, and being himself,
Slow, and unquestioned,
And inordinately there, O stoic!
Wandering in the slow triumph of his own existence,
Ringing the soundless bell of his presence in chaos,
And biting the frail grass arrogantly,
Decidedly arrogantly.

Kangaroo

In the northern hemisphere
Life seems to leap at the air, or skim under the wind
Like stags on rocky ground, or pawing horses, or springy scut-
tailed rabbits.

Or else rush horizontal to charge at the sky's horizon,
Like bulls or bisons or wild pigs.

Or slip like water slippery towards its ends,
As foxes, stoats, and wolves, and prairie dogs.

Only mice, and moles, and rats, and badgers, and beavers, and
perhaps bears
Seem belly-plumbed to the earth's mid-navel.
Or frogs that when they leap come flop, and flop to the centre
of the earth.

But the yellow antipodal Kangaroo, when she sits up,
Who can unseat her, like a liquid drop that is heavy, and just
touches earth.
The downward drip
The down-urge.
So much denser than cold-blooded frogs.

Delicate mother Kangaroo
Sitting up there rabbit-wise, but huge, plumb-weighted,
And lifting her beautiful slender face, oh! so much more gently
and finely lined than a rabbit's, or than a hare's,
Lifting her face to nibble at a round white peppermint drop
which she loves, sensitive mother Kangaroo.

Her sensitive, long, pure-bred face.
Her full antipodal eyes, so dark,

So big and quiet and remote, having watched so many empty
    dawns in silent Australia.

Her little loose hands, and drooping Victorian shoulders.
And then her great weight below the waist, her vast pale belly
With a thin young yellow little paw hanging out, and straggle
    of a long thin ear, like ribbon,
Like a funny trimming to the middle of her belly, thin little
    dangle of an immature paw, and one thin ear.

Her belly, her big haunches
And, in addition, the great muscular python-stretch of her tail.

There, she shan't have any more peppermint drops.
So she wistfully, sensitively sniffs the air, and then turns, goes
    off in slow sad leaps

On the long flat skis of her legs,
Steered and propelled by that steel-strong snake of a tail.

Stops again, half turns, inquisitive to look back.
While something stirs quickly in her belly, and a lean little face
    comes out, as from a window,
Peaked and a bit dismayed,
Only to disappear again quickly away from the sight of the
    world, to snuggle down in the warmth,
Leaving the trail of a different paw hanging out.

Still she watches with eternal, cocked wistfulness!
How full her eyes are, like the full, fathomless, shining eyes of
    an Australian black-boy
Who has been lost so many centuries on the margins of exist-
    ence!

She watches with insatiable wistfulness.
Untold centuries of watching for something to come,
For a new signal from life, in that silent lost land of the South.

48

Where nothing bites but insects and snakes and the sun, small
   life.
Where no bull roared, no cow ever lowed, no stag cried, no
   leopard screeched, no lion coughed, no dog barked,
But all was silent save for parrots occasionally, in the haunted
   blue bush.

Wistfully watching, with wonderful liquid eyes.
And all her weight, all her blood, dripping sack-wise down to-
   wards the earth's centre,
And the live little-one taking in its paw at the door of her belly.

Leap then, and come down on the line that draws to the earth's
   deep, heavy centre.

The Blue Jay

The blue jay with a crest on his head
Comes round the cabin in the snow.
He runs in the snow like a bit of blue metal,
Turning his back on everything.

From the pine-tree that towers and hisses like a pillar of shaggy
    cloud
Immense above the cabin
Comes a strident laugh as we approach, this little black dog
    and I.
So halts the little black bitch on four spread paws in the snow
And looks up inquiringly into the pillar of cloud,
With a tinge of misgiving.
Ca-a-a! comes the scrape of ridicule out of the tree.

What voice of the Lord is that, from the tree of smoke?

Oh, Bibbles, little black bitch in the snow,
With a pinch of snow in the groove of your silly snub nose,
What do you look at *me* for?
What do you look at me for, with such misgiving?

It's the blue jay laughing at us.
It's the blue jay jeering at us, Bibs.

Every day since the snow is here
The blue jay paces round the cabin, very busy, picking up bits,
Turning his back on us all,
And bobbing his thick dark crest about the snow, as if darkly
    saying:
I ignore those folk who look out.

You acid-blue metallic bird,
You thick bird with a strong crest,
Who are you?
Whose boss are you, with all your bully way?
You copper-sulphate blue bird!

Man, Woman, Child

Piano

Softly, in the dusk, a woman is singing to me;
Taking me back down the vista of years, till I see
A child sitting under the piano, in the boom of the tingling
    strings
And pressing the small, poised feet of a mother who smiles as
    she sings.

In spite of myself, the insidious mastery of song
Betrays me back, till the heart of me weeps to belong
To the old Sunday evenings at home, with winter outside
And hymns in the cosy parlour, the tinkling piano our guide.

So now it is vain for the singer to burst into clamour
With the great black piano appassionato. The glamour
Of childish days is upon me, my manhood is cast
Down in the flood of remembrance, I weep like a child for the
    past.

Peach

Would you like to throw a stone at me?
Here, take all that's left of my peach.

Blood-red, deep;
Heaven knows how it came to pass.
Somebody's pound of flesh rendered up.

Wrinkled with secrets
And hard with the intention to keep them.

Why, from silvery peach-bloom,
From that shallow-silvery wine-glass on a short stem
This rolling, dropping, heavy globule?

I am thinking, of course, of the peach before I ate it.

Why so velvety, why so voluptuous heavy?
Why hanging with such inordinate weight?
Why so indented?

Why the groove?
Why the lovely, bivalve roundnesses?
Why the ripple down the sphere?
Why the suggestion of incision?

Why was not my peach round and finished like a billiard ball?
It would have been if man had made it.
Though I've eaten it now.

But it wasn't round and finished like a billiard ball.
And because I say so, you would like to throw something at me.

Here, you can have my peach stone.

Discord in Childhood

Outside the house an ash-tree hung its terrible whips,
And at night when the wind rose, the lash of the tree
Shrieked and slashed the wind, as a ship's
Weird rigging in a storm shrieks hideously.

Within the house two voices arose, a slender lash
Whistling she-delirious rage, and the dreadful sound
Of a male thong booming and bruising, until it had drowned
The other voice in a silence of blood, 'neath the noise of the
   ash.

End of Another Home Holiday

When shall I see the half-moon sink again
Behind the black sycamore at the end of the garden?
When will the scent of the dim white phlox
Creep up the wall to me, and in at my open window?

Why is it, the long, slow stroke of the midnight bell
   (Will it never finish the twelve?)
Falls again and again on my heart with a heavy reproach?
The moon-mist is over the village, out of the mist speaks the
    bell,

And all the little roofs of the village bow low, pitiful, beseech-
    ing, resigned.
—Speak, you my home! what is it I don't do well?

At home, suddenly I love you
As I hear the sharp clean trot of a pony down the road,
Succeeding sharp little sounds dropping into silence
Clear upon the long-drawn hoarseness of a train across the
    valley.

.   .   .   .   .   .

The light has gone out, from under my mother's door.
    That she should love me so!—
    She, so lonely, greying now!
    And I leaving her,
    Bent on my pursuits!

        Love is the great Asker.
        The sun and the rain do not ask the secret
        Of the time when the grain struggles down in the dark.
        The moon walks her lonely way without anguish,
        Because no one grieves over her departure.

Forever, ever by my shoulder pitiful love will linger,
Crouching as little houses crouch under the mist when I turn.
Forever, out of the mist, the church lifts up a reproachful finger,
Pointing my eyes in wretched defiance where love hides her
    face to mourn.

        Oh! but the rain creeps down to wet the grain
        That struggles alone in the dark,
        And asking nothing, patiently steals back again!
        The moon sets forth o' nights
        To walk the lonely, dusky heights
        Serenely, with steps unswerving;
        Pursued by no sigh of bereavement,

60

No tears of love unnerving
Her constant tread:
While ever at my side,
Frail and sad, with grey, bowed head,
The beggar-woman, the yearning-eyed
Inexorable love goes lagging.

The wild young heifer, glancing distraught,
With a strange new knocking of life at her side
    Runs seeking a loneliness.
The little grain draws down the earth, to hide.
Nay, even the slumberous egg, as it labours under the shell
    Patiently to divide and self-divide,
Asks to be hidden, and wishes nothing to tell.

But when I draw the scanty cloak of silence over my eyes
Piteous love comes peering under the hood;
Touches the clasp with trembling fingers, and tries
To put her ears to the painful sob of my blood;
While her tears soak through to my breast,
    Where they burn and cauterise.

· · · · · ·

The moon lies back and reddens.
In the valley a corncrake calls
    Monotonously,
With a plaintive, unalterable voice, that deadens
    My confident activity;
With a hoarse, insistent request that falls
    Unweariedly, unweariedly,
    Asking something more of me,
        Yet more of me.

The Best of School

The blinds are drawn because of the sun,
And the boys and the room in a colourless gloom
Of underwater float: bright ripples run
Across the walls as the blinds are blown
To let the sunlight in; and I,
As I sit on the shores of the class, alone,
Watch the boys in their summer blouses
As they write, their round heads busily bowed:
And one after another rouses
His face to look at me,
To ponder very quietly,
As seeing, he does not see.

And then he turns again, with a little, glad
Thrill of his work he turns again from me,
Having found what he wanted, having got what was to be had.

And very sweet it is, while the sunlight waves
In the ripening morning, to sit alone with the class
And feel the stream of awakening ripple and pass
From me to the boys, whose brightening souls it laves
For this little hour.

     This morning, sweet it is
To feel the lads' looks light on me,
Then back in a swift, bright flutter to work:
Each one darting away with his
Discovery, like birds that steal and flee

Touch after touch I feel on me
As their eyes glance at me for the grain
Of rigour they taste delightedly.

As tendrils reach out yearningly,
Slowly rotate till they touch the tree
That they cleave unto, and up which they climb
Up to their lives—so they to me.

I feel them cling and cleave to me
As vines going eagerly up; they twine
My life with other leaves, my time
Is hidden in theirs, their thrills are mine.

The Collier's Wife

Somebody's knockin' at th' door
   Mother, come down an' see!
—I's think it's nobbut a beggar;
   Say I'm busy.

It's not a beggar, mother; hark
   How 'ard 'e knocks!
—Eh, tha'rt a mard-arsed kid,
   'E'll gie thee socks!

Shout an' ax what 'e wants,
   I canna come down.
—'E says, is it Arthur Holliday's?
   —Say Yes, tha clown.

'E says: Tell your mother as 'er mester's
   Got hurt i' th' pit—
What? Oh my Sirs, 'e never says that.
   That's not it!

Come out o' th' way an' let me see!
   Eh, there's no peace!
An' stop thy scraightin', childt,
   Do shut thy face!

"Your mester's 'ad a accident
   An' they ta'ein' 'im i' th' ambulance
Ter Nottingham."—Eh dear o' me,
   If 'e's not a man for mischance!

Wheer's 'e hurt this time, lad?
   —I dunna know,
They on'y towd me it wor bad—
   It would be so!

Out o' my way, childt! dear o' me, wheer
   'Ave I put 'is clean stockin's an' shirt?
Goodness knows if they'll be able
   To take off 'is pit-dirt!

An' what a moan 'e'll make! there niver
   Was such a man for fuss
If anything ailed 'im; at any rate
   I shan't 'ave 'im to nuss.

I do 'ope as it's not very bad!
   Eh, what a shame it seems
As some should ha'e hardly a smite o' trouble
   An' others 'as reams!

It's a shame as 'e should be knocked about
   Like this, I'm sure it is!
'E's 'ad twenty accidents, if 'e's 'ad one;
   Owt bad, an' it's his!

There's one thing, we s'll 'ave a peaceful 'ouse
      f'r a bit,
   Thank heaven for a peaceful house!
An' there's compensation, sin' it's accident.
   An' club-money—I won't growse.

An' a fork an' a spoon 'e'll want—an' what else?
   I s'll never catch that train!
What a traipse it is, if a man gets hurt!
   I sh'd think 'e'll get right again.

Celebrations
and
Condemnations

Conundrums

Tell me a word
that you've often heard,
yet it makes you squint
if you see it in print!

Tell me a thing
that you've often seen,
yet if put in a book
it makes you turn green!

Tell me a thing
that you often do,
which described in a story
shocks you through and through!

Tell me what's wrong
with words or with you
that you don't mind the thing
yet the name is taboo.

Thought

Thought, I love thought.
But not the jaggling and twisting of already existent ideas
I despise that self-important game.
Thought is the welling up of unknown life into consciousness,
Thought is the testing of statements on the touchstone of the
    conscience,
Thought is gazing on to the face of life, and reading what can
    be read,
Thought is pondering over experience, and coming to con-
    clusion.
Thought is not a trick, or an exercise, or a set of dodges,
Thought is a man in his wholeness wholly attending.

River Roses

By the Isar, in the twilight
We were wandering and singing,
By the Isar, in the evening
We climbed the huntsman's ladder and sat swinging
In the fir-tree overlooking the marshes,
While river met with river, and the ringing
Of their pale-green glacier water filled the evening.
By the Isar, in the twilight
We found the dark wild roses
Hanging red at the river; and simmering
Frogs were singing, and over the river closes
Was savour of ice and of roses; and glimmering
Fear was abroad. We whispered: "No one knows us.
Let it be as the snake disposes
Here in this simmering marsh."

How Beastly the Bourgeois Is

How beastly the bourgeois is
especially the male of the species—

Presentable eminently presentable—
shall I make you a present of him?

Isn't he handsome? isn't he healthy? Isn't he a fine specimen?
doesn't he look the fresh clean englishman, outside?
Isn't it god's own image? tramping his thirty miles a day
after partridges, or a little rubber ball?
wouldn't you like to be like that, well off, and quite the thing?

Oh, but wait!
Let him meet a new emotion, let him be faced with another
      man's need,
let him come home to a bit of moral difficulty, let life face him
      with a new demand on his understanding
and then watch him go soggy, like a wet meringue.
Watch him turn into a mess, either a fool or a·bully.
Just watch the display of him, confronted with a new demand
      on his intelligence,
a new life-demand.

How beastly the bourgeois is
especially the male of the species—

Nicely groomed, like a mushroom
standing there so sleek and erect and eyeable—
and like a fungus, living on the remains of bygone life
sucking his life out of the dead leaves of greater life than his
      own.

And even so, he's stale, he's been there too long.
Touch him, and you'll find he's all gone inside

just like an old mushroom, all wormy inside, and hollow
under a smooth skin and an upright appearance.

Full of seething, wormy, hollow feelings
rather nasty—
How beastly the bourgeois is!

Standing in their thousands, these appearances, in damp
    England
what a pity they can't all be kicked over
like sickening toadstools, and left to melt back, swiftly
into the soil of England.

Reading in the Evening

I have sat in the recreation ground
Under an oak tree whose yellow buds dotted the pale blue sky:
The young grass twinkled in the wind, and the sound
Of the wind hung round the knotted buds like a canopy.

I have travelled in Russia two hours or more,
No, a long season I have been with Dostoïevsky in the dark
Ways of St Petersburg, I have dwelled in the core
Of Russia, through the new great naïveté of Russia, her wide
    sad child eyes so clear.

Now to the Recreation Ground
I am come back a foreigner, wondering and shrinking from the
    scene
From the noise of children playing around
From the tulips coloured with chalk, and the dull grass' evening
    green.

How lonely in the wide world is this playground,
How lonely, under the tree; unnoticed.

Bare Fig-trees

Fig-trees, weird fig-trees
Made of thick smooth silver,
Made of sweet, untarnished silver in the sea-southern air—
I say untarnished, but I mean opaque—
Thick, smooth-fleshed silver, dull only as human limbs are dull
With the life-lustre,
Nude with the dim light of full, healthy life
That is always half-dark,
And suave like passion-flower petals,

Like passion-flowers,
With the half-secret gleam of a passion-flower hanging from the
    rock,
Great, complicated, nude fig-tree, stemless flower-mesh,
Flowerily naked in flesh, and giving off hues of life.

Rather like an octopus, but strange and sweet-myriad-limbed
    octopus;
Like a nude, like a rock-living, sweet-fleshed sea-anemone,
Flourishing from the rock in a mysterious arrogance.

Let me sit down beneath the many-branching candelabrum
That lives upon this rock
And laugh at Time, and laugh at dull Eternity,
And make a joke of stale Infinity,

Within the flesh-scent of this wicked tree,
That has kept so many secrets up its sleeve,
And has been laughing through so many ages
At man and his uncomfortablenesses,
And his attempt to assure himself that what is so is not so,
Up its sleeve

Let me sit down beneath this many-branching candelabrum,
The Jewish seven-branched, tallow-stinking candlestick kicked
     over the cliff
And all its tallow righteousness got rid of,
And let me notice it behave itself.

And watch it putting forth each time to heaven,
Each time straight to heaven,
With marvellous naked assurance each single twig.
Each one setting off straight to the sky
As if it were the leader, the main-stem, the forerunner,
Intent to hold the candle of the sun upon its socket-tip,
It alone.

Every young twig
No sooner issued sideways from the thigh of his predecessor
Than off he starts without a qualm
To hold the one and only lighted candle of the sun in his
     socket-tip.

He casually gives birth to another young bud from his thigh,
Which at once sets off to be the one and only,
And hold the lighted candle of the sun.

Oh many-branching candelabrum, oh strange up-starting fig-
     tree,
Oh weird Demos, where every twig is the arch twig,
Each imperiously over-equal to each, equality over-reaching
     itself

Like the snakes on Medusa's head,
Oh naked fig-tree!

Still, no doubt every one of you can be the sun-socket as well as
every other of you.
Demos, Demos, Demos!
Demon, too,
Wicked fig-tree, equality puzzle, with your self-conscious secret
fruits.

The Great Newspaper Editor
to His Subordinate

Mr Smith, Mr Smith
haven't I told you to take the pith
and marrow and substance out of all
the articles passing beneath your scrawl?

And now look here what you've gone and done!
You've told them that life isn't really much fun,
when you know that they've got to think that they're happy,
as happy as happy, Oh, so happy, you sappy.

Think of the effect on Miss Harrison
when she reads that her life isn't really much fun.
She'll take off her specs. and she'll put down the paper
as if it was giving off poison vapour.

And she'll avoid it; she'll go and order
The Morning Smile, sure that it will afford her
comfort and cheer, sure that it will tell her
she's a marv'lous, delicious, high-spirited feller.

You must chop up each article, make it pappy
and easy to swallow; always tell them they're happy,
suggest that they're spicy, yet how *pure* they are,
and what a sense of true humour they've got, ha-ha!

Mr Smith, Mr Smith,
have you still to learn that pith
and marrow and substance are sure to be
indigestible to Miss Ponsonby!

Mr Smith, Mr Smith
if you stay in my office, you've got to be kith
and kin with Miss Jupson, whose guts are narrow
and can't pass such things as substance and marrow.

Mr Smith, Mr Smith
consider Miss Wilks, or depart forthwith.
For the British Public, once more be it said,
is summed up in a nice, narrow-gutted old maid.

Elemental

Why don't people leave off being lovable
or thinking they are lovable, or wanting to be lovable,
and be a bit elemental instead?

Since man is made up of the elements
fire, and rain, and air, and live loam
and none of these is lovable
but elemental,
man is lop-sided on the side of the angels.

I wish men would get back their balance among the elements
and be a bit more fiery, as incapable of telling lies
as fire is.

I wish they'd be true to their own variation, as water is,
which goes through all the stages of steam and stream and ice
without losing its head.

I am sick of lovable people,
somehow they are a lie.

At the Window

The pine-trees bend to listen to the autumn wind as it mutters
Something which sets the black poplars ashake with hysterical
    laughter;
As slowly the house of day is closing its eastern shutters.

Farther down the valley the clustered tombstones recede,
Winding about their dimness the mist's grey cerements, after
The street-lamps in the twilight have suddenly started to bleed.

The leaves fly over the window, and utter a word as they pass
To the face that gazes outwards, watching for night to waft a
Meaning or a message over the window glass.

A Rose Is Not a Cabbage

And still, in spite of all they do, I love the rose of England,
but the cabbages of England leave me cold.

Oh the cabbages of England leave me cold
even though they grow on genuine English mould,
with their caterpillars, and the care with which they fold
nothingness, pale nothingness in their hearts.

Now that the winter of our discontent
is settled on the land, roses are scarce in England, very scarce,
    there are none any more.
But look at the cabbages, Oh count them by the score!
Oh aren't they green. Oh haven't we, haven't we spent
a lot of money rearing them———!

Yet the cabbages of England leave me cold
no matter of what sort the cabbage be.

Things Made by Iron

Things made by iron and handled by steel
are born dead, they are shrouds, they soak life out of us.
Till after a long time, when they are old and have steeped in
   our life
they begin to be soothed and soothing: then we throw them
   away.

All-knowing

All that we know is nothing, we are merely crammed waste-
   paper baskets
unless we are in touch with that which laughs at all our
   knowing.

Andraitx—Pomegranate Flowers

It is June, it is June
the pomegranates are in flower,
the peasants are bending cutting the bearded wheat.

The pomegranates are in flower
beside the high road, past the deathly dust,
and even the sea is silent in the sun.

Short gasps of flame in the green of night, way off
the pomegranates are in flower,
small sharp red fires in the night of leaves.

And noon is suddenly dark, is lustrous, is silent and dark
men are unseen, beneath the shading hats;
only, from out the foliage of the secret loins
red flamelets here and there reveal
a man, a woman there.

The Ignoble Procession

When I see the ignoble procession
streaming forth from little doorways
citywards, in little rivers that swell to a great stream,
of men in bowler hats, hurrying
and a mingling of wallet-carrying women
hurrying, hurrying, legs going quick quick quick
in ignoble haste, for fear of being late—
I am filled with humiliation.

Their haste
is so
humiliating.

Last Hours

The cool of an oak's unchequered shade
Falls on me as I lie in deep grass
Which rushes upward, blade beyond blade.
While higher the darting grass-flowers pass
Piercing the blue with their crocketed spires
And waving flags, and the ragged fires
Of the sorrel's cresset—a green, brave town
Vegetable, new in renown.

Over the tree's edge, as over a mountain
Surges the white of the moon,
A cloud comes up like the surge of a fountain,
Pressing round and low at first, but soon
Heaving and piling a round white dome.
How lovely it is to be at home
Like an insect in the grass
Letting life pass!

There's a scent of clover crept through my hair
From the full resource of some purple dome
Where that lumbering bee, who can hardly bear
His burden above me, never has clomb.
But not even the scent of insouciant flowers
Makes pause the hours.
Down the valley roars a townward train.
I hear it through the grass
Dragging the links of my shortening chain
Southwards, alas!

The Oxford Voice

When you hear it languishing
and hooing and cooing and sidling through the front teeth,
        the oxford voice
          or worse still
        the would-be oxford voice
you don't even laugh any more, you can't.
For every blooming bird is an oxford cuckoo nowadays,
you can't sit on a bus nor in the tube
but it breathes gently and languishingly in the back of your
    neck.
And oh, so seductively superior, so seductively
        self-effacingly
        deprecatingly
        superior.—
We wouldn't insist on it for a moment
        but we are
          we are
        you admit we are
        superior.——

When I Went to the Film

When I went to the film, and saw all the black-and-white
    feelings that nobody felt,
and heard the audience sighing and sobbing with all the
    emotions they none of them felt,
and saw them cuddling with rising passions they none of them
    for a moment felt,
and caught them moaning from close-up kisses, black-and-white
    kisses that could not be felt,
It was like being in heaven, which I am sure has a white
    atmosphere
upon which shadows of people, pure personalities
are cast in black and white, and move
in flat ecstasy, supremely unfelt,
and heavenly.

After the Opera

Down the stone stairs
Girls with their large eyes wide with tragedy
Lift looks of shocked and momentous emotion up at me.
And I smile.

Ladies
Stepping like birds with their bright and pointed feet
Peer anxiously forth, as if for a boat to carry them out of the
    wreckage;
And among the wreck of the theatre crowd
I stand and smile.
They take tragedy so becomingly;
Which pleases me.

But when I meet the weary eyes
The reddened, aching eyes of the bar-man with thin arms,
I am glad to go back to where I came from.

Sick

I am sick, because I have given myself away.
I have given myself to the people when they came
so cultured, even bringing little gifts,
so they pecked a shred of my life, and flew off with a croak
of sneaking exultance.
So now I have lost too much, and am sick.

I am trying now to learn never
to give of my life to the dead,
never, not the tiniest shred.

Bavarian Gentians

Not every man has gentians in his house
in soft September, at slow, sad Michaelmas.

Bavarian gentians, big and dark, only dark
darkening the day-time, torch-like with the smoking blueness of
    Pluto's gloom,
ribbed and torch-like, with their blaze of darkness spread blue
down flattening into points, flattened under the sweep of white
    day
torch-flower of the blue-smoking darkness, Pluto's dark-blue
    daze,
black lamps from the halls of Dis, burning dark blue,
giving off darkness, blue darkness, as Demeter's pale lamps give
    off light,
lead me then, lead the way.

Reach me a gentian, give me a torch!
let me guide myself with the blue, forked torch of this flower
down the darker and darker stairs, where blue is darkened on
    blueness
even where Persephone goes, just now, from the frosted Septem-
    ber
to the sightless realm where darkness is awake upon the dark
and Persephone herself is but a voice
or a darkness invisible enfolded in the deeper dark
of the arms Plutonic, and pierced with the passion of dense
    gloom,
among the splendour of torches of darkness, shedding darkness
    on the lost bride and her groom.

D*

Love

Search for Love

Those that go searching for love
only make manifest their own lovelessness,

and the loveless never find love,
only the loving find love,
and they never have to seek for it.

Flapper

Love has crept out of her sealèd heart
   As a field-bee, black and amber,
   Breaks from the winter-cell, to clamber
Up the warm grass where the sunbeams start.

Mischief has come in her dawning eyes,
   And a glint of coloured iris brings
   Such as lies along the folded wings
Of the bee before he flies.

Who, with a ruffling, careful breath,
   Has opened the wings of the wild young sprite?
   Has fluttered her spirit to stumbling flight
In her eyes, as a young bee stumbleth?

Love makes the burden of her voice.
   The hum of his heavy, staggering wings
   Sets quivering with wisdom the common things
That she says, and her words rejoice.

Green

The dawn was apple-green,
    The sky was green wine held up in the sun,
The moon was a golden petal between.

She opened her eyes, and green
    They shone, clear like flowers undone
For the first time, now for the first time seen.

Fidelity

Fidelity and love are two different things, like a flower and a
    gem.
And love, like a flower, will fade, will change into something
    else
or it would not be flowery.

O flowers they fade because they are moving swiftly; a little
    torrent of life
leaps up to the summit of the stem, gleams, turns over round
    the bend
of the parabola of curved flight,
sinks, and is gone, like a comet curving into the invisible.

O flowers they are all the time travelling
like comets, and they come into our ken
for a day, for two days, and withdraw, slowly vanish again.

And we, we must take them on the wing, and let them go.
Embalmed flowers are not flowers, immortelles are not flowers;
flowers are just a motion, a swift motion, a coloured gesture;
that is their loveliness. And that is love.

But a gem is different. It lasts so much longer than we do
so much much much longer
that it seems to last forever.
Yet we know it is flowing away
as flowers are, and we are, only slower.
The wonderful slow flowing of the sapphire!

All flows, and every flow is related to every other flow.
Flowers and sapphires and us, diversely streaming.

In the old days, when sapphires were breathed upon and
    brought forth

during the wild orgasms of chaos
time was much slower, when the rocks came forth.
It took æons to make a sapphire, æons for it to pass away.

And a flower it takes a summer.

And man and woman are like the earth, that brings forth
	flowers
in summer, and love, but underneath is rock.
Older than flowers, older than ferns, older than foraminiferæ
older than plasm altogether is the soul of a man underneath.

And when, throughout all the wild orgasms of love
slowly a gem forms, in the ancient, once-more-molten rocks
of two human hearts, two ancient rocks, a man's heart and a
	woman's,
that is the crystal of peace, the slow hard jewel of trust,
the sapphire of fidelity.
The gem of mutual peace emerging from the wild chaos of
	love.

Roses on the Breakfast Table

Just a few of the roses we gathered from the Isar
Are fallen, and their mauve-red petals on the cloth
Float like boats on a river, while other
Roses are ready to fall, reluctant and loth.

She laughs at me across the table, saying
I am beautiful. I look at the rumpled young roses
And suddenly realize, in them as in me,
How lovely is the self this day discloses.

Intimates

Don't you care for my love? she said bitterly.

I handed her the mirror, and said:
Please address these questions to the proper person!
Please make all requests to headquarters!
In all matters of emotional importance
please approach the supreme authority direct!—
So I handed her the mirror.

And she would have broken it over my head,
but she caught sight of her own reflection
and that held her spellbound for two seconds
while I fled.

Bei Hennef

The little river twittering in the twilight,
The wan, wondering look of the pale sky,
   This is almost bliss.

And everything shut up and gone to sleep,
All the troubles and anxieties and pain
   Gone under the twilight.

Only the twilight now, and the soft "Sh!" of the river
   That will last for ever.

And at last I know my love for you is here;
I can see it all, it is whole like the twilight,
It is large, so large, I could not see it before,
Because of the little lights and flickers and interruptions,
   Troubles, anxieties and pains.

You are the call and I am the answer,
You are the wish, and I the fulfillment,
You are the night, and I the day.
   What else? it is perfect enough.
   It is perfectly complete,
   You and I,
   What more——?

Strange, how we suffer in spite of this!

In a Boat

See the stars, love,
In the water much clearer and brighter
Than those above us, and whiter,
Like nenuphars!

Star-shadows shine, love:
How many stars in your bowl?
How many shadows in your soul?
Only mine, love, mine?

When I move the oars, see
How the stars are tossed,
Distorted, even lost!
Even yours, do you see?

The poor waters spill
The stars, waters troubled, forsaken!—
The heavens are not shaken, you say, love;
Its stars stand still.

There! did you see
That spark fly up at us? even
Stars are not safe in heaven!
What of me then, love, me?

What then, love, if soon
Your star be tossed over a wave?
Would the darkness look like a grave?
Would you swoon, love, swoon?

Spring Morning

Ah, through the open door
Is there an almond-tree
Aflame with blossom!
    —Let us fight no more.

Among the pink and blue
Of the sky and the almond flowers
A sparrow flutters.
    —We have come through,

It is really spring!—See,
When he thinks himself alone
How he bullies the flowers.
    —Ah, you and me

How happy we'll be!—See him?
He clouts the tufts of flowers
In his impudence
    —But, did you dream

It would be so bitter? Never mind,
It is finished, the spring is here.
And we're going to be summer-happy
    And summer-kind.

We have died, we have slain and been slain,
We are not our old selves any more.
I feel new and eager
    To start again.

It is gorgeous to live and forget.
And to feel quite new.
See the bird in the flowers?—he's making
    A rare to-do!

He thinks the whole blue sky
Is much less than the bit of blue egg
He's got in his nest—we'll be happy,
    You and I, I and you.

With nothing to fight any more—
In each other, at least.
See, how gorgeous the world is
    Outside the door!

Index of First Lines

A man should never earn his living,   32
A snake came to my water-trough   18
Ah, through the open door   116
All that we know is nothing, we are merely crammed
     waste-paper baskets   90
And still, in spite of all they do, I love the rose of England,   88
Butterfly, the wind blows sea-ward, strong beyond the
     garden wall!   42
By the Isar, in the twilight   73
Climbing through the January snow, into the Lobo Canyon   39
Don't you care for my love? she said bitterly.   112
Down the stone stairs   98
Fidelity and love are two different things, like a flower
     and a gem   109
Fig-trees, weird fig-trees   78
How beastly the bourgeois is   74
I am sick, because I have given myself away.   98
I can imagine, in some otherworld   17
I have sat in the recreation ground   76
I never saw a wild thing   38
In the northern hemisphere   47
It is June, it is June   92
Just a few of the roses we gathered from the Isar   111
Love has crept out of her sealèd heart   106

Mr Smith, Mr Smith   83
Not every man has gentians in his house   101
On he goes, the little one,   44
Outside the house an ash-tree hung its terrible whips 58
See the stars, love,   115
Softly, in the dusk, a woman is singing to me;   55
Somebody's knockin' at th' door   65
Tell me a word   71
The blinds are drawn because of the sun,   62
The blue jay with a crest on his head   50
The cool of an oak's unchequered shade   94
The dawn was apple-green,   108
The elephant, the huge old beast,   22
The little river twittering in the twilight,   114
The pine-trees bend to listen to the autumn wind
    as it mutters   86
Things made by iron and handled by steel   90
Those that go searching for love   105
Thought, I love thought.   72
When did you start your tricks,   34
When I see the ignoble procession   93
When I went into my room, at mid-morning,   24
When I went to the film, and saw all the black-and-white
    feelings that nobody felt,   97
When shall I see the half-moon sink again   59
When you hear it languishing   96
Why don't people leave off being lovable   85
Would you like to throw a stone at me?   57